The
Christmas Dishes

By Linda Garber

Share your love.

Linda Garber

ISBN-13: 978-0-9885561-0-2
Library of Congress Control Number: 2012922388

With special thanks to Ella Garber and Lucas Garber
Design by Greentree Graphics, Middlebury, IN 46540

Printed by Evangel Press,
2000 Evangel Way, Nappanee, Indiana 46550-0189
www.evangelpress.com

Printed in the United States of America

To order please visit www.evangelauthorservices.com
or call 1-800-253-9315

10 9 8 7 6 5 4 3 2 1

"Thank-you! Thank-you, Mom and Dad!" I squealed.
Those dishes would fit perfectly in the orange crate
cupboard they had made for me!

All too soon the last gift had been opened and admired.
It was time to get ready for the big family Christmas dinner.

The Phillips family annual Christmas get-together
was so much fun! I had 14 cousins; nine were
girls who were close to my age.

The year that I was seven, I considered Christmas the most wonderful time of the year–singing in our school Christmas program, helping Grandma make cookies and candy, the parties, the twinkling lights, and the gifts. Oh, yes the gifts!

Tasting the cookies before we shared
them with others was fun, too!

Harvest on the farm had been good that autumn of 1955, with lots of grain to fill the giant bins and silos.

Mom had purchased a few new shiny glass ornaments for the Christmas tree, and its top just brushed our farmhouse ceiling. That tree smelled like you were walking through a pine forest! Somehow it seemed there were more brightly wrapped gifts under the tree this year.

December 25
Christmas Day was finally here!

Dad had finished milking the cows, and our family gathered in the big kitchen to eat the delicious breakfast Mom had prepared. It was always special on Christmas morning!

It was our family's tradition to read the story of the birth of Jesus from the Bible–we did it every year on Christmas morning. Next we sang our favorite carols, "Silent Night, Holy Night," and "Away in the Manager."

And at last it was time to open our gifts!

We took turns unwrapping our
presents so that we could,
"ooh," and "ah," over each, and I
could barely wait for my brother
and sister to finish opening each
gift when it was their turn. My sister
carefully unwrapped each gift without
tearing the paper, folding it carefully
so the paper could be used again.
And my little brother was not nearly
fast enough! It seemed to take forever!

I really needed the pink flannel pajamas, and the new socks and mittens could replace my old ones that had holes in the toes and fingers.

Then Dad walked into the room carrying something large. Lately he and Mom had been spending time out in the shop, and now I discovered why. They had used a wooden orange crate from the grocery store to build a cupboard for me. It was painted red and white, and would look beautiful in my bedroom.

But

I knew

there would still

be a *Special* gift

for me to open, hidden

somewhere under the

tree.

Then Mom very carefully handed me a gift. It was wrapped in bright red paper with a green, red and white bow. I couldn't take my time as my sister did. In my excitement I gripped that red wrapping paper and ripped it away.

Inside I found the most beautiful dishes I had ever seen.
They were painted with a blue and white pattern and were
so delicate! I lifted out each tiny dish. The small plate fit in
the palm of my hand. The creamer and sugar had the
tiniest lids! They were wonderful!

Each year my mother and her sisters took turns hosting the holiday event. One year Aunt Helen invited us to her home; the next year was Aunt Dene's turn. Then everyone would come to our house, and the fourth year the whole family traveled to Aunt Louise's home. Life was never dull when the cousins were together!

As Mom checked on the turkey roasting in the oven, and Dad set up extra tables and chairs, I looked again at my brand new dishes. How beautiful they were! The cups made little clinking sounds when they touched each other. It would be so much fun to have tea parties with my dolls.

I thought about what my girl cousins would say
when they saw such a treasured gift.

I also wondered how they would treat my beautiful new china
dishes when we played in the afternoon. These dishes were
so special–I had never had anything like them. My
cousins would be careful, wouldn't they?

What if the younger girls wanted
to play with them?

The more I thought about those dishes,
the more I worried about them.

I finally decided it would be best to hide my new dishes!

Since we lived in a very old farmhouse, there were no
closets in our house. Mom and Dad had a large armoire in
their bedroom–a very tall, very long piece of furniture
where they hung their clothing. Hiding my dishes
on top of that armoire was the perfect solution!

At first I crawled up on a chair, but that armoire was very,
very tall. I didn't come close to reaching its top.

I added a small stool to the chair, and then piled 2 big books
on the stool. Now I was ready! This time I lifted the dishes, and
by stretching as much as I could, I pushed the box of dishes
with my fingertips up over the edge of that big armoire.

Just when the box began to slide over the
top edge, those big books slipped.

The chair fell.

The stool fell.

The books fell.

I fell.

The box fell.

The dishes fell.

CRASH!

We landed on the hard
wooden floor in my
parent's bedroom.

"No! My dishes!" I cried.

After sifting through all the little broken pieces on the floor, the only surviving dishes were 1 cup, 1 saucer, the sugar bowl, and its lid. The rest of my lovely dishes, my very best Christmas gift the year I was 7 years old, had shattered into tiny pieces.

Is this a true story?   Yes.

Did Dad and Mom buy me more dishes?

Noooooooooo, not for a looooooooong time.

But, did they love me? YES!

Very, very much!

Today on the shelf in my bedroom are sitting 1 blue and white cup, 1 saucer, 1 sugar bowl and its lid. They are the same dishes I received more than 50 years ago. When I look at them I remember the very best gift I received the Christmas I was 7–I learned how important it is to share.

The End

...and my cousins
still have fun
together.

Linda Garber loved growing
up on the family farm in
northern Indiana. She taught
social studies, and then
became a school library
media specialist. She received
the Esther Burrin Award
from the Association of
Indiana Media Educators
for outstanding
library programs.

Dedicated to

1 supportive husband, Steve

+ 2 loving parents, Dean and Rosemary Williams

+ 3 special children: Kori Cripe, Tyler Garber and Ross Garber
along with their spouses: Troy, Heidi and Kelly

6 adorable grandkids, Gage, Ella, Malia, Lucas, Anna, & Allie

Questions for Discussion

What is the worst thing that could happen if the girl in our story shared her dishes with her cousins?

What could she say to them about the dishes before they played?

Should her parents buy her more dishes?

Do you remember a time when you chose not to share? How did you feel?

What are ways you can share with someone? It is not always "things."

What would you do if a group did not share with one person? It may be not letting someone have a turn.

Have you ever been forced to share something? How did you feel?

Are there things we don't have to share?

What hurtful behaviors do you see that you could change?

What qualities do you look for in a friend?